Horizons

The Fox in the Box

Horizons Phonics and Reading 1
Reader 1

Author:	Polly A. Wood, M.A.
Editor:	Alan L. Christopherson, M.S.
Illustrations:	Karen Eubanks, Steve Ring,
	Jeri Reed, Greg Capps,
	Kirk Headley, Seth McCullough,
	Karn Crysdale, Brian McCracken
Layout Design:	Lauren Durain, A.S.T.

Alpha Omega Publications, Inc. • Rock Rapids, IA

©MMI by Alpha Omega Publications, Inc.

804 N. 2nd Ave. E.
Rock Rapids, IA 51246-1759
800-622-3070
www.aop.com

Printed in the United States of America

ISBN 978-0-7403-0321-0

A Note to Teachers and Parents

The Horizons First Grade Phonics Readers are to be used as a companion to the Horizons First Grade Student Workbooks. For each lesson in the Student Workbooks there is a corresponding story in the Readers. The story will illustrate and demonstrate the primary concept of the lesson. Most first grade students should not be expected to read the first forty stories independently. The teacher or parent should read the stories to the student. The student can sound out some of the shorter, single syllable words. After lesson forty, most first grade students should be able to start reading the stories independently. The student may still require some help with some of the words. The teacher or parent should make word cards for the words that the student does not know. The word cards should be reviewed with the student frequently. As the student's vocabulary increases, the student may be able to go back to the first forty stories and read them independently.

The teacher or parent should ask the student questions before and after reading the story. Help the student anticipate what is going to happen in the story after reading the title or looking at the pictures. There are comprehension questions at the end of each story. The answers to these questions should be discussed. If so desired, the teacher or parent may have the student write out the answers to the questions.

At this stage, the skill level of each student will vary. It is not necessary for the student to sound out and read every word in a story. This skill will develop gradually over the course of this unit. Enjoy the learning process as it happens!

Table of Contents

Lesson #	Title	Page

Dan's Dog

Dan had a dog. The dog's name was Peppy. Peppy was a small dog. His fur was tan, with some white spots. Peppy was a good dog most of the time. He did not mess up the house, and did what he was told.

One morning, Dan was getting ready for school. He was running a little late, because he hadn't gotten up when his dad told him to. He stayed in bed too long. He quickly ate his breakfast and brushed his teeth. He chose a shirt from his closet and a pair of shorts from

his drawer. Dan heard his dad calling him, so he went to see what Dad wanted.

When Dan returned to his room, he was puzzled. Where were the shirt and shorts that he had gotten out to wear? Dan looked for them. He looked everywhere in his room. No shirt and shorts. He looked in the bathroom. No shirt and shorts there, either. Dan was getting worried, because he was really going to be late for school!

Just as he went into his room to choose something else to wear, Peppy came running out of the hallway. Peppy ran into Dan's room. He was carrying the shirt and the shorts in his mouth!

13

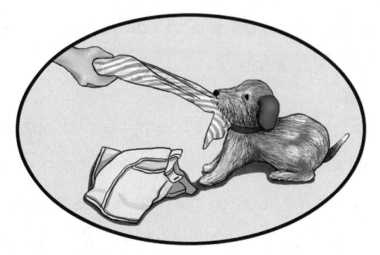

Dan laughed and tried to get the clothes away from Peppy. That silly dog wouldn't let Dan have them. He ran back down the hall, with Dan right behind him. Peppy was having fun being chased!

Into the living room they ran. Dan was very confused and surprised, because Peppy had never done anything like this before.

Dan called to his dad, "Dad! Help me get my clothes from Peppy!" Dan's dad ran into the living room just in time to grab Peppy and snatch the shirt and shorts from Peppy's mouth. Peppy barked in delight. That had been such fun!

"What has gotten into that dog?" Dan's dad asked in surprise.

"I don't know, but I'd better go and get dressed. I'm going to be late for school!" Dan exclaimed.

Dan got dressed in a hurry and headed out the front door for school. Peppy sat by the front window watching him. It had been an exciting morning for him!

1. Why was Dan worried at the beginning of the story?
2. How did Peppy normally act?
3. Why was Dan so surprised by what Peppy did?
4. Who helped Dan get his clothes back?

Jim and the Soccer Ball

Jim got a soccer ball for his seventh birthday. He loved the ball and played with it every day after school. His friend Mike often came over and played with it also.

One day, they decided to go to the park and play. They were kicking the ball back and forth to each other. They were having a great time. Jim and Mike did not notice that three older boys were watching them play with the ball. The older boys came over to Jim and Mike.

One of the boys said, "We want to play, too."

Another one said, "Yes, we do not have a ball and we want to play with yours."

Jim did not know what to do because he was scared of the older boys.

Jim said, "Okay. You can play with my ball for a while if you promise to give it back. Mike and I will watch you."

The older boys played with the ball for what seemed like a very long time. Pretty soon, it was time for Jim and Mike to go home. Jim told the boys that he had to go home, and he needed to have his ball back. The boys did not want to give the ball back to Jim.

The biggest boy said, "We still want to play with it.

Come back later and we will give it to you."

Jim felt sick. He had not known that this would happen. He was scared. But he knew that he must be brave and stand up for what was right.

Jim said, "I need my ball back now, please. I have to go home and I will get into trouble if I do not go home on time. Please keep your word and give me back my ball."

The older boys all looked at one another. Jim was sure that they were not going to give the ball back, even though he had asked for it nicely.

The big boy said, "You can have your ball. We will just find another one."

And with that, they all walked away. Jim and Mike walked home, feeling good because they had done the right thing and stood up for themselves without fighting.

1. What did the older boys want? Why did they want it?
2. What would you do if you were Jim?

The Cat in the Van

Jane and her mom were getting ready to go to the grocery store. They walked out the door to get in their van. Mom had forgotten her purse, so she went back in the house. She had left the door to the van open. Jane tossed her ball in the air while she waited for her mom.

While Mom was in the house and Jane was playing, a cat saw that the door to the van was open. The cat was curious. He crept closer to the open door. Jane did not see him. The cat sneaked into the van and crouched on the floor of the back seat.

Jane's mom came out of the house with her purse.

"Let's go!" she called to Jane.

Jane and her mom got in the van and drove to the grocery store, which was only a few minutes away from their house.

The cat was feeling scared, since he did not know where he was or where he was going. He felt that he should not have been so curious about the van. He thought about meowing to be let out, but he was afraid of the strangers in the van. They were not his family.

When he felt the van stop, he was very scared. He wanted to get out. He decided that meowing was the only way.

"Meow! Meow!" he said.

Jane turned around in her seat.

"Mom!" she cried, "Look on the floor behind you!"

Mom turned around to look. She was so surprised to see the cat that she let out a little scream.

Jane said, "Don't be afraid, mom. He is just scared. I'll bet that he got in after you left your door open to go get your purse."

Mom said, "You're right. And he is somebody's pet. We'd better head back home and let him go. Someone is probably missing their cat!"

Mom backed out of the parking space and drove home. When they got there, Jane opened the side door to the van. The cat jumped out right away. He was so happy to be free!

1. Why did the cat go into the van?
2. Was the cat happy that he went in the van?
   Why, or why not?
3. What would you do if you found an animal in your car or van?

Nan's Hat

Nan had a black hat. It was small, but very nice. She wore it to church on Sunday. Her mom and dad did not let her wear it to school because it might get messed up.

One Sunday, as Nan and her family were leaving church, the wind came up. It blew Nan's hat right off of her head. The hat went flying away.

Nan ran after it as fast as she could. The hat landed in some grass. Nan grabbed it before the wind blew it again.

Mom had run over to help Nan get her hat. She was happy when she saw that Nan had her hat.

Mom said, "Maybe we should get a strap for that hat so that it will stay on your head."

Nan said, "I think I will not wear my hat on windy days."

Mom thought that was a good idea.

1. Where did Nan like to wear her hat?
2. Why did the hat blow off of her head?
3. What did Mom want to do with the hat?

The Nice Bike

When Brian turned five years old, he decided that he had gotten to be too big for his trike. He wanted a real bike. He told his mom and dad about it. They said that they would go to the toy store and look for a bike.

The next Saturday, Brian and his mom and dad went to the store to get his bike. There were so many to choose from! Brian could not decide. He finally picked out a white one with black trim on it. When he went to try it out, he found out that it was too high for him. His feet would not touch the ground, and that was not safe.

Then, they found a blue one that Brian liked. It was shiny and not too high for him.

Brian said, "This is a nice bike. I like it. I think that I would like to buy this one."

Dad said, "Yes, this is a nice bike. If you like it so much, then this is the one we will get."

When Brian got home, he invited his friend Mike over to ride bikes. They had a great time. Brian was so happy with his bike!

1. Why did Brian want a bike?
2. Why didn't Brian buy the first bike that he liked?
3. What did the one he bought look like?
4. What did Brian do when he got home?

Nate Skates

Nate had always wanted to learn to ice skate.
He thought that playing on the ice would be fun.
His parents agreed to start taking him for lessons.

At the first skating lesson, his teacher, Mr. Blake, taught Nate how to glide on the ice. Nate got the hang of it right away. It was fun. Next, Mr. Blake showed Nate how to skate backward. Nate had some trouble with this. He waited until Mr. Blake had shown him many times before he tried it on his own.

Soon, Nate had learned how to skate forward and backward in one lesson. Nate could have skated all day, but his first lesson was over, and it was time to go.

Even the rain outside could not make him feel badly. He was so happy that he was learning to skate.

The next day, he went to the rink and practiced. He could not stay away. He came back for his next lesson and did just great!

1. What did Nate learn at his first skating lesson?
2. What did Nate do the day after his first lesson?
3. Do you think that Nate will become a good skater? Why or why not?

Cecelia Goes to the City

Cecelia and her family lived on a farm in the country. They raised cattle and chickens. They had a horse named Gypsy and a cat named Ginger. They had a vegetable garden and grew geraniums in their flower garden. The family worked hard on their farm. There was always a lot of work to do.

In the summer, the family decided that they wanted to go to the city for a vacation. They got Cecelia's Uncle Cyril to come and stay to do the work on the farm while they were away.

Cecelia had such a good time in the city. She and her family visited museums and went to movies. Cecelia especially liked the circus that she and her family went to see. They even went to the zoo, where they saw the tallest giraffe they had ever seen! They ate in restaurants and went to an outdoor market. They saw giant buildings hundreds of feet tall!

When the week was over and it was time to go back to the farm, Cecelia and her family were sad, but they were ready to go back to their work on the farm. They were happy because they had great memories of their exciting trip to the city.

1. Where did Cecelia and her family live?
2. Where did they go on vacation?
3. What were some of the things that they did on vacation?
4. What would you like to do if you visited a big city?

Lee's Teeth

Lee started losing his baby teeth when he was five years old. The first one that he lost was one of his front teeth on the top. The tooth was loose for a week. Lee spent the whole week wiggling the loose tooth until it finally came out.

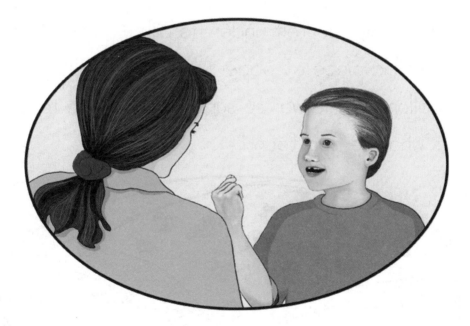

Lee's mom told him that he would get a treat for a lost tooth. She told him to put the tooth under his pillow when he went to sleep that night, and he would find a surprise under his pillow the next morning.

That night Lee was so excited that he had a hard time sleeping. His mom reminded him that the treat would not come if he was not asleep. He counted sheep for awhile and fell asleep.

In the morning, Lee felt under his pillow. He thought that he felt a piece of paper. When he looked, he saw a dollar bill! He was so surprised! He ran to tell his parents what he had found.

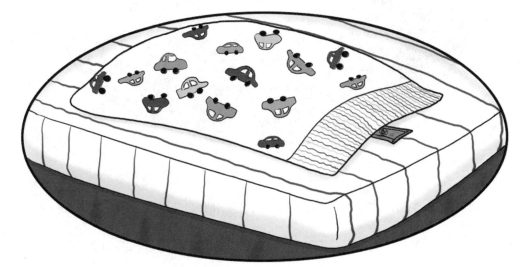

Dad said, "That's a very nice treat for a lost tooth!"

Mom said, "Save your dollar. I'm sure that you will be getting more loose teeth, and that might mean more treats under your pillow! You could buy yourself something really great after losing all of those teeth!"

Lee agreed. He decided to save the dollar. He went to the bathroom to look in the mirror to see if he had any more loose teeth.

1. How old was Lee when he lost his first tooth?
2. What did Lee's mom tell him to do with his tooth?
3. What did Lee decide to do with his dollar?
4. What would you do with the dollar?

The Peach Tree

Jean and her brother, Keith, had a peach tree in their backyard. It was a small tree, called a dwarf peach tree. It had been there in the yard when their family moved into the house.

Every spring, the tree grew beautiful pink flowers. In the summer, the flowers grew into peaches. The peaches were sweet and juicy. The tree usually had many peaches by the end of the summer, more peaches than the family could eat at one time. Mom would can the peaches so that the family could have peaches to eat in the winter. She would also make peach jam and dried peaches.

It was Jean's and Keith's job to keep the tree watered and trimmed. They did a good job. They knew that it was important to take care of the tree so that they could have delicious peaches to eat.

One summer, the tree starting growing peaches from the flowers, just as it had always done. But Jean and Keith began noticing that the small, hard, green peaches that the tree began the summer with, were disappearing day by day. Jean and Keith could not figure out what was happening to the peaches.

Then, one day, as Jean was going out of the back door to water the tree, she noticed something strange. Their dog, Blacky, was jumping up into the tree. As he jumped, he bit peaches off the tree! She had never seen him do that before. Jean ran at the dog, yelling at him to get away from the tree. Blacky sat there, crunching on a green peach.

She told Mom and Dad what had happened. After that, the family decided that they needed to put a wire fence around the tree to keep the dog away.

Mom said, "How strange that we have never seen him do this before."

Dad said, "Maybe he tried a peach that had fallen from the tree and decided that he liked them."

There were not as many peaches to eat that year as there had been in other years. The dog, however, surely did have his share!

1. What kind of a peach tree did Jean and Keith have in their yard?
2. What were the jobs that Jean and Keith did to take care of the tree?
3. What was the strange thing that happened with the tree?
4. How did the family solve the problem?

The Old Goat

Joe had an old goat. Joe did not know just how old the goat was. Joe had gotten the goat from his grandpa. Grandpa did not want to keep the goat on his farm anymore, so he gave it to Joe. Joe's family had a very big back yard and could have large animals.

When Joe first got the goat, he decided to name her Flo. Flo moved very slowly because she was old. She liked it when Joe petted her and talked to her.

One summer day, Joe was mowing the grass, which was his weekly chore in the summer. He noticed that Flo was acting funny, like she was afraid of something. Joe turned off the mower and went over to Flo. She calmed down right away. Joe sat and talked to her for awhile, and she seemed fine. He went back to his mowing. After a few minutes, he looked over at Flo again. She seemed very nervous. He stopped mowing and went over to her again. This time, he looked around to see if there were any other animals around that might be scaring Flo. There were no other animals. Flo calmed down and he went back to mowing.

Just as he was starting the mower, Flo did something that Joe had never seen her do before. She charged right at him! Joe stopped mowing and quickly turned off the mower. As soon as the motor was quiet, Flo stopped charging and was calm.

"Aha!" Joe said to himself, "She does not like the loud sound of the mower! I will have to find another place to put Flo when I am mowing."

Joe told his mom about the problem. She said that he could put Flo in the big shed when he was mowing.

1. How did Joe get Flo?

2. What was the problem that Joe and Flo were having?

3. Do you think that putting Flo in the shed solved the problem?

4. What would you do if you were Joe?

Racing

Tim and Eric were good runners. They liked to run at school and at the park. They ran in races. They were very fast.

One day in P.E. class at school, Mr. James, the P.E. teacher, said that they were going to have a race to see who the fastest boy and girl were in the class. Tim and Eric couldn't wait for the race to start.

All of the boys lined up. Mr. James yelled, "On your mark, get set, go!"

The boys ran down the field and around the tree. As they were running back to the starting line, Tim and Eric were right next to each other.

Tim yelled, "I'm going to win!"

Eric yelled back, "No, I'm going to win!"

As they reached the end of the race, Lauren ran past both of them. Tim crossed the finish line just ahead of Eric.

"Good job, Lauren," said Mr. James.

All of the kids in the class cheered for her. Eric and Tim were surprised, but cheered for her, too.

"Yes, we're glad for you," said Eric.

"That's right," said Tim. "I wish that one of us could've won the race."

Mr. James said, "You both did a good job, too."

"It was fun," said Tim. "Maybe next time one of us will win."

1. What did Tim and Eric like to do?
2. What did they do in P.E. class?
3. How did the boys act when Lauren won?

Mike's Kite

Mike had a blue kite. He liked to fly his kite on windy days. His younger sister Pat went with him. She had a green kite. They watched the wind take their kites sailing through the sky.

One day, when they were flying their kites at the park, a bad thing happened. Mike was not watching where he was flying his kite. He was so excited about the way that it was flying that he got the kite caught in a tree. Pat saw what happened. She ran over to Mike.

Pat said, "How did that happen?"

Mike said, "I was just flying my kite and the next thing that I knew, I had flown it right into this tree."

Pat said, "You stay here with your kite. I will go and get some help."

Pat ran home and got their dad. He loaded his tallest ladder into his truck. He and Pat drove back to the park and found the tree where Mike's kite was stuck.

Dad asked, "How did you do that?"

Pat said, "I asked him the same question."

Mike said, "I guess that I was not paying attention to where I was flying my kite. I got so excited."

Dad said, "Well, let's just get this kite down."

Dad got his ladder out of the back of the truck. He carried it over and stood it up against the tree trunk.

It was just tall enough to reach the branch where the kite was caught. Dad climbed up the ladder and reached over to get the kite out. He untangled the string and pulled the kite out of the branches.

"Thanks, Dad!" Mike shouted.

Dad said, "Please be more careful next time. I may not be around to help you, and it could be dangerous for you to get it yourself."

Mike said, "I will, Dad. Thanks again for helping me."

1. What did Mike and his sister Pat like to do?
2. What happened when Mike wasn't watching?
3. How did the story end?

The Big Backyard

We have a big backyard. We like to play in it.
We like it because it has a lot of grass and trees.
We invite our friends over to play.

There is a doghouse for our dog, Pepper. Pepper likes to play in the sunshine. He also likes to dig in our sandbox, which is not always good!

Mom lets us have snacks in the backyard. We have peanuts and popcorn. Sometimes we even have cupcakes. We can also eat our breakfast on the patio. We have pancakes or oatmeal.

When it rains, we can play outside, if it is not raining too hard. We make sure that we wear our raincoats. The grass gets wet and we have to be careful not to run in it. Sometimes there are puddles, and we make little walnut shell sailboats to float in them.

We like to play with our toys in our backyard. We keep a backpack full of toys that we like to play with back there. We have a special railroad train set that we can play with outside. We set the tracks up on the patio.

We have a lot of fun in our big backyard. We hope that we will always live here.

1. Why do the children like their backyard so much?

2. Write down all of the compound words that you can find in the story.

3. How many compound words did you find?

Kim and the Roses

One spring day, Kim's mother was planting roses in her garden. Kim came outside. She asked her mother if she could help her plant the roses.

"Yes, you can help me by digging some small holes for me to plant the roses in," Mother said.

"May I put the roses in the holes?" Kim asked.

Mother said, "Okay, but be careful when you are putting the roses in the holes. I will tell you which roses to put in which holes."

"I can do it by myself," said Kim.

"No, I need to help you at first. Then we will see if you can do it by yourself," said Mother.

But Kim did not listen to her mother. When mother went into the garage to get more roses, Kim started digging up the roses that Mother had already planted. She dug four holes over by the tree.

Then she got four of the roses that she had dug up and planted them by the tree. She dug three holes next to the fence. She got three of the roses that she had dug up and planted them there.

Just as Kim was about to dig more holes next to the fence, Mother came out of the garage with her arms full of rose plants.

"Oh, my!" Mother gasped, "Kim, what are you doing?"

"I wanted to plant the roses in different places," said Kim. "I didn't think that those roses looked pretty where you had them."

"You need to go in the house for awhile. You did not listen to me when I told you to let me help you first," said Mother.

"I am sorry, mother," said Kim. "I only wanted to help."

"Well, maybe you can help me a little later. For now, I want you to understand that it is important to listen to me and do as I tell you to do," Mother said.

Kim had learned an important lesson that day. She learned that Mother was doing what was best for her. She would do a better job of listening to her mother from then on.

1. What did Kim do that was wrong?
2. Why do you think that Kim did the wrong thing?
3. Do you think that she will listen in the future?

Bill and Jeff

Bill and Jeff are brothers. Bill is in second grade and Jeff is in fourth grade. Bill and Jeff are alike in some ways, and different in other ways.

One of the ways that they are different is in their height. Bill is actually taller than Jeff! Their parents say that Bill takes after Dad's side of the family because all of the people on Dad's side are tall. He has two brothers and one sister. Dad is the tallest member of his family.

The people on Mom's side of the family are shorter. Mom and Dad say that Jeff is like Mom's side of the family because he is not tall.

Bill likes to play games outside. He is a jumper. He likes to jump. Jeff also likes to play outside, but he is not a jumper. He is a runner. He is the fastest runner in the family.

Bill and Jeff like to play tag outside. Jeff usually wins because is a faster runner. Bill wins the jumping games.

Bill and Jeff know that being alike in some ways and different in other ways is okay. They are good friends as well as brothers.

1. Why is it strange that Bill is taller than Jeff?
2. What is one way that Bill and Jeff are alike?
3. What is one way that Bill and Jeff are different?

Baking Cookies

Jill liked to make things. She really liked to cook and bake. One day, she decided to bake cookies. She asked her mom if it was all right.

Mom said, "That sounds like fun. Why don't you call Kim and ask her if she would like to come over and help you?"

Jill said, "That would be great. Thanks, Mom!"

Jill was excited. She called Kim and asked her to come over and help with the cookies.
Kim said, "It is okay with my mom. I will be right over!"

When Kim got there, Jill was getting things ready. Mom had turned the oven on so that it would be hot enough to bake the cookies when they were ready.

The girls used a recipe that Mom had given them. It was for chocolate chip cookies, which were Jill's favorite. Jill and Kim were taking turns mixing the butter, eggs, flour, sugar, vanilla, and finally, adding the chocolate chips. They had fun making the cookies. Mom liked the way that they shared the spoon.

Jill and Kim made sure they did things the safest way that they could. They had Mom put the cookie sheets in the hot oven. Mom also took the cookie sheets out of the oven when the cookies were all done baking.

When some of the cookies were cool, Jill and Kim sat down at the kitchen table to eat a few of them. They also drank some milk with their cookies.

Jill said, "It sure is fun making cookies."

Kim said, "Yes, and it is almost more fun eating them!"

1. What did Jill and Kim do that was fun?
2. How did Jill and Kim take turns?
3. How did Jill and Kim make sure that they did things the safest way that they could?
4. What is your favorite kind of cookie?

Mark's Scooter

Mark wanted a scooter for his birthday. He thought that it would be fun to ride. He could see himself riding so fast that it would feel like he was flying.

Mark told his parents that he wanted a scooter for his birthday.

Mom said, "You would have to be very careful. Those things can be very dangerous."

Dad said, "Yes. If you fell, it would be painful."

Still, Mark was hopeful that he would get the scooter. He thought about it every night before he went to sleep. He knew that he could be careful. He would wear special pads on his elbows and knees and, of course, he would wear his helmet.

Finally, his birthday came. His parents had a party for him. Five of his good friends were there. His grandparents were also there. He was thankful to everyone for being at his party.

After Mark had opened what he thought were all of his presents, Mom and Dad had one last surprise for him. Dad went into the garage and came back with a shiny, new silver scooter! Mark cried out in surprise.

"Thanks Mom and Dad!" Mark shouted. "I wasn't sure if I would get this. You were both fearful that I would not be careful. I promise that I will wear my pads and ride carefully."

"We know that you will," Mom said. "We know that you will be careful when you ride your scooter."

Dad said, "Just make sure that you ride when Mom or I are watching you."

"I will. Thanks so much Mom and Dad. This is the best birthday present that I have ever had," said Mark.

1. Why were Mark's parents afraid of getting him a scooter?
2. What did Mark promise his parents?
3. Do you think that Mark will ride safely, as he promised?

The Frosty Night

Ned loved winter. He loved the snow and the cold weather. All of his friends liked summer the best, but Ned liked the shivery feeling that the chilly air of winter gave him.

One night in December, it was especially frosty. As Ned looked out of his bedroom window, he noticed that there was no wind, and the cold just seemed to hang in the air. There was about a foot of snow on the ground, the kind of wet snow that was just right for making a snowman.

Ned went to ask his dad if he could go out and make a snowman. He was not frightened of the darkened sky. With the porch light on, he would be able to see very well.

Dad asked, "Are you sure that you want to go out in the cold tonight? Why don't you wait until tomorrow?"

"I don't mind the cold air. I want to make the snowman tonight, because by morning, it will be hardened, and it will last longer," Ned said.

Dad said, "Well, all right. Just don't stay out too long. I will be out to check on you in a little while."

Ned pulled on his coat, gloves, hat, and boots and went out the front door. It had gotten windy since he had looked out of his window before. It was colder than he had thought it would be, too.

He rolled the first ball of snow, which was the biggest one. It would be the base for the snowman. He patted the big, round ball with his hands to pack it so that it would be smooth. Then, he rolled the medium-sized ball for the body, and the smallest ball for the head. The head would be a suitable size for a hat. He added sticks for the arms and got some pieces of charcoal for the buttons and eyes. The last thing that he did was to add a smile to the face.

Ned stepped back to look at his snowman. He liked the friendly way that he looked. Just then, Dad came out of the front door.

"That is a fine looking snowman, Ned. It's very cold, though. Why don't you come inside now and you can look at him some more tomorrow," Dad said.

"Okay," said Ned.
"I am thirsty for some hot chocolate."

Ned and Dad went inside and had the best hot chocolate that they had ever had.

1. Why did Ned want to make the snowman at night?
2. Why did Ned like winter so much?
3. What is your favorite season, and why do you like it the best?

Going Shopping

Mary and her grandma were going shopping for food. Grandma needed a lot of things, so she asked Mary to help her. Mary liked to go shopping with her grandma.

As they drove to the grocery store, they talked about the things that they would buy.

Grandma said, "I will need a loaf of bread and a gallon of milk. I will also need one dozen eggs, pancake mix, and a pound of flour."

Mary wrote everything down on a piece of paper as Grandma told her all of the groceries that they would need to buy.

When Mary and Grandma were at the store, they got a shopping cart and started looking for the things that Grandma needed. Everything was easy to find,

except for the pancake mix. They looked in the part of the store that had the baking needs. Then, they checked the part of the store that had the breads. They just could not find it. They asked a man who worked in the store if he knew where they could find pancake mix.

The man said, "It is in with the flour and the sugar, where the baking needs are located."

Grandma said, "We checked there, but we could not find it."

The man said, "Let me come with you and we will look together."

Mary, Grandma, and the man who worked in the store walked over to the part of the store that had the flour and the sugar. There it was! The pancake mix was on the bottom shelf, right next to the brown sugar.

Grandma said, "Well! I must need new glasses! I looked right past it!"

Mary cried, "Grandma! You are not wearing your glasses! You took them off before we got out of the car!"

The man said, "Maybe that was the problem!"

They all laughed as Mary put the pancake mix in the cart. She and Grandma thanked the man and went off to the check-out stand to pay for the groceries.

1. Why did Grandma ask Mary to go shopping with her?
2. What was the problem that Mary and Grandma had in the store?
3. How did they solve the problem?

Kay's Kitten

Kay found a kitten. The kitten was black and white. She knew that the kitten was not very old because it was little. The kitten was sitting in a box in front of the grocery store where Kay's family did their grocery shopping.

Kay saw the kitten as she and her mom were coming out of the store. Kay ran to it and picked it up. She took it to her mom. Mom wanted to make sure that the kitten did not belong to someone else. They went back into the store and asked the manager if he knew of anyone who had called the store about a lost kitten. The man said that no one had called or come in about a kitten.

Kay felt sorry for the kitten and wanted so much to take it home to keep. Her mom was happy to let her keep it. She was sure that they could give it a good home.

Kay and her mom took the kitten home. They named the kitten "Lucky" because they thought that they

were lucky to have found it. And the kitten was lucky
to have such a loving family to take care of it.

1. What did Kay find?
2. Where did she find it?
3. What did Kay and her mom want to make sure of before
   they took the kitten home?
4. Why do you think that Kay felt sorry for it?
5. How did the story end?

Paul's Book

On Monday, Paul went to the library with his first grade class. Each child got to check out one book. Paul chose a book about dogs.

Paul took the book home that day. He had his mom read the book to him, and then he read the book all by himself. Paul liked the book. It had many pictures of different kinds of dogs. He put the book on the shelf in his room when he was not reading it so that it would not get lost.

Paul and his class were to go back to the library the next Monday. They were to take the books back that they checked out before. Then, each child could check out a different book. When Paul looked in his desk for the book, he could not find it. He got upset. He told his teacher, Mrs. Shaw.

Mrs. Shaw said, "Maybe it is in your backpack. Go look in there."

Paul looked in his backpack, but the book was not there either. He did not know what to do. If he did not have the book, he could not check out another one.

Paul asked his friend, Taylor, if he had seen the book.

"Yes," said Taylor, "You let me read it after school on Friday. I took it home with me."

"Is it still at your house?" asked Paul.

"No, I have it right here," said Taylor. He handed the book to Paul. Paul felt much better.

"Thanks, Taylor. I forgot that I let you read my book. I am glad that you remembered to bring it to school today," said Paul. "Did you like the book?" Paul asked.

"Yes, I did. It had a lot of good pictures of dogs. I would like to check that book out today when you take it back to the library," said Taylor.

"Maybe this time I can borrow your book," said Paul.

1. What was Paul's book about?
2. Why did Paul like the book?
3. What happened the day that Paul's class was to go back to the library?
4. How was the problem solved?

The Rainy Day

Jean and her little brother, Jay, were sitting in Jean's room one Saturday morning. It was a rainy day. They were upset because they could not go outside.

Jean asked, "What we can do?"

Jay said, "Maybe we can play a game."

They played a card game called "Go Fish." After they had played for a while, they did not want to play anymore. They turned on the TV, but there was nothing on that they liked.

Mom said, "Why don't you two call Grandma? You have not talked to her in weeks."

"Okay!" said Jean. She was happy to talk to Grandma. Grandma lived in a town far away. Jean and Jay got to see her only a few times a year.

After Mom dialed Grandma's phone number, she gave Jean the phone.

"Hello, Grandma. This is Jean."

"Why, hello! It is good to hear from you!" said Grandma.

Jay got on the phone in the kitchen. He said hello to Grandma too. They had a nice talk. Jean and Jay told Grandma what they had been doing in school. Jay told her about the soccer game that his team had won last Saturday. Jean told Grandma about her dance class. When it was time to hang up, they all said good-bye.

"Well," said Jean, "This has turned out to be a nice day after all. Thanks for letting us talk to Grandma, Mom. That was a good idea."

1. Why were Jean and Jay upset?
2. What did they try doing to have fun?
3. What did Mom have them do that was fun?
4. What do you like to do on rainy days?

The Elephant at the Zoo

Jenny and her friend, John, went to the zoo. John's mom took them on a Sunday afternoon. They went to see all of the animals. They saw lions, tigers, monkeys, and many kinds of birds.

The animal that Jenny and John liked the best was the elephant. This elephant was a female. She was big and gray and had a very long trunk.

Jenny said, "This elephant is the biggest animal I have ever seen!'

John said, "Well, elephants are the biggest land animals on Earth."

"I like to watch the elephant. She does funny things," Jenny said.

The elephant was throwing water all over herself with her trunk. She looked like she was having a lot of fun. It was a hot day, and this was her way of cooling herself off.

"I wish that I could do that," John said.

"Yes, it would feel great," said Jenny.

They stood and watched the elephant walk around and eat. Then, she played with the water some more. After awhile, it was time to go home.

"It is time to go home now," John's mom said. "Maybe we can come back some time soon."

"Next time, I want to see the elephant first!" Jenny said.

"So do I," said John. "She is my favorite animal."

1. What animals did Jenny and John see at the zoo?
2. What was the elephant doing that was funny?
3. What is your favorite zoo animal?

The Column of Numbers

Tony was learning to add numbers in math class. It was easy at first, because he was adding two numbers at a time. The teacher gave the class problems like 2 + 2 and 4 + 4. Tony liked those kinds of problems.

One day the teacher told the class that they were going to learn something new. They were going to learn to add more than two numbers at a time. She wrote 3 + 2 + 5= ? on the chalkboard. Tony did not know the answer. His teacher told the class to write the problem down on their papers and try to add the numbers. Tony wrote the problem down, but did not know what to do next.

Tony said, "Mrs. Jones, I do not know how to do this."

Mrs. Jones looked around the room. Most of the kids in the class were looking at her as if they did not know what to do either.

Mrs. Jones said, "Oh, my! I had better do this problem on the chalkboard for you. Here is the way to do this problem."

She showed the class the right way to add the column of numbers. She told them to add the first two numbers, then add the next number to that answer. Everyone seemed to understand.

Tony said, "Now I get it! Can we do another one just like that?"

"Yes. We will do many more of those," said Mrs. Jones. "I am glad that you know how to do this now."

Tony felt much better. Math was fun again!

1. What was Tony learning to do in math class?

2. What happened when Mrs. Jones tried to teach the class to add the new way?

3. How did Mrs. Jones solve the problem?

Brenda's Phone

Stephanie shared a bedroom with her older sister, Brenda. Brenda went to high school and had lots of friends. She was always talking to her  friends on the phone. Brenda did not want Stephanie in their room when she was on the phone. Stephanie was not happy about this.

One night, Brenda had been on the phone for what seemed like a very long time. Stephanie wanted to be in the room, too, but Brenda would not let her.

Stephanie told Mom what was going on.

Mom said, "I will go and talk to Brenda."

"It is not fair that I can't be in the room when she is on the phone!" said Stephanie.

"I know it's not," said Mom.

Mom went to the girls' bedroom and told Brenda to hang up the phone. Brenda did as she was told.

"Brenda, you share a room with Stephanie. She is to be let in the room at all times," Mom said. "From now on, your phone time is five minutes per call."

Brenda said, "But Mom, that is not enough time!"

Mom said, "That is the way that it is going to be for a while. I am sorry that you do not like it.

"I am sorry. I was not being fair," Brenda said.

Stephanie said, "I am glad that I will be able to be in our room again."

Brenda said, "Let's play a game together, Stephanie. How about Monopoly?"

From then on, Brenda spent less time on the phone and more time with her family.

1. What was Brenda doing that was not fair?
2. What did Stephanie do about it?
3. How was the problem solved?

The Tick of the Clock

Jan's mom put a clock in Jan's bedroom. She wanted Jan to be able to get herself up in the morning. The clock was a round clock with an alarm.

Jan did not like the clock because it ticked so loudly. She told her mom about the clock.

Jan said, "Mom, I do not like this clock that you gave me."

Mom asked, "Why not?"

Jan said, "It ticks so loudly that I cannot sleep at night."

Mom said, "We can try it another night and see how it goes. I want you to be able to wake yourself up in the morning. You need an alarm clock to do that."

Jan said, "All right. I will try it one more night."

That night, Jan was lying in bed. She could hear the loud ticking of the clock. She tried to ignore it. She tried to go to sleep. After what seemed like a very long time, Jan got up and  went out to the kitchen where her mom was.

"Mom," Jan said, "that clock just ticks too loudly. I cannot sleep. I tried to ignore it, but I cannot. May I please have a different clock?"

Mom said, "We don't have any other clocks. I will have to go and get one for you tomorrow. I will wake you up myself tomorrow morning."

"Thanks, Mom. Now, may I go and get some sleep?" Jan asked.

1. What problem did Jan have with her clock?
2. What did Jan's mom tell her to do?
3. How was the problem finally solved?

The Rough Road

The Smith family lived in the country. The road to their house was made of dirt. It was a rough road. When it rained, the road got very muddy. The Smith's truck had a tough time going down the road after it rained.

One night, there was a rainstorm. The Smith family was coming back from town. When the Smiths got on the road to their house, the truck began to slide. The road was muddy and slick. Before they knew it, the members of the Smith family and their truck were in the ditch. Dad and their oldest boy, Dave, tried to push the truck out, while Mom tried to steer. Just as soon as they almost got the truck out, it slid back into the ditch. Dad and Dave decided to walk to the closest house and call a tow truck. It was not fun to walk in the wind and the rain.

Because of the storm, it took the tow truck a long time to get there. While they waited, the Smith family tried to make the best of it by telling funny stories. They laughed and laughed! Finally, the tow truck arrived.

After they were safely home again, Mr. and Mrs. Smith decided that it was time to pave the rough road that led to their house. No more muddy rides for them!

1. What was the road that led to the Smith's house like?
2. What bad thing happened on the road?
3. What did the Smiths do about it?

The Circus

Jack and Jen liked to go to the circus. They loved the clowns. Jack liked the rough way that the clowns played. They always knocked each other down. They made Jack laugh.

Jen liked the colorful costumes that the clowns wore. Some of them had ruffled collars around their necks. Jen thought that the collars were pretty.

Jen and Jack also liked the popcorn at the circus. Their mom and dad always bought some for them to share. One big bag was enough for both of them.

Mom liked the trapeze artists. She liked the way that they seemed to fly through the air. It was really something the way that they caught each other in mid-air.

Dad liked the animals. He liked the tricks that the dogs and the horses did. It was fun to watch them as they jumped and turned in the air.

Jen, Jack, and their parents go to the circus whenever it is in town. They always have a great time.

1. What did Jack like at the circus?
2. What did Jen like at the circus?
3. What did Mom and Dad like at the circus?
4. What is your favorite part of the circus?

The Beaver

Did you know that beavers like to eat wood? They eat the bark from trees and use trees in many other ways.

Beavers have large front teeth so that they can gnaw on the wood. They gnaw on the trunks of trees. The trees fall down and the beavers use them to build their homes.

They also use the trees to build dams. The dams stop the water in streams and rivers. The beavers build their homes partly under water.

If you are in the forest and you see small tree trunks that look as if they have been gnawed and chewed upon, that might be a sign that beavers were there.

1. Why do beavers have such large front teeth?

2. What are some of the uses that beavers have for trees?

Sir John, the Knight

There once lived a brave knight named Sir John. He wore a shiny suit of armor. Sir John was brave and fought in many of the king's battles. One day, he wished to speak with the king.

"What can I do for you, Sir John?" the king asked as Sir John knelt before him.

"Sire, I have served you for many years. I am getting old and tired. I have fought many of the king's battles and have served him in great danger. Sire, I wish to stop fighting."

The king thought about the old knight's wish and said, "Sir John, you are the best knight in my kingdom. You are brave, strong, and have won many battles, but, if you wish to stop fighting, you may. I can see you have thought about this a long time."

"Thank you, sire," Sir John said. "I know you are doing the right thing."

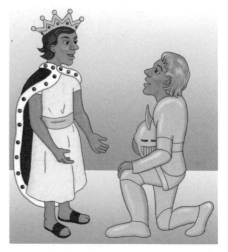

"However," the king added, "you must help me find a brave knight to take your place."

"Yes, your majesty," Sir John replied. "Thank you."

Sir John stood up, bowed, and went home. He took off his sword. He leaned it next to the fireplace. He knew he would not need it much longer. He felt a little sad, but he knew that the king had other brave knights, and one of them would fill his place.

1. Why did Sir John want to stop fighting in battles?
2. Did the king let him stop?
3. How did Sir John feel about not fighting anymore?

The Lamb Who Liked to Climb

Joe lived on a farm. There were many animals on the farm, but Joe's favorite was a lamb named Snowy. Snowy got his name because his wooly coat was so white.

Snowy liked to get out of the sheep's pen. He liked to run around the pasture. When he did this, Joe's dad would come to get Joe so that he could get Snowy and put him back in the sheep's pen.

Joe could not see how Snowy was getting out of the pen. The gate was never open, except when someone went in the pen to feed the sheep. Even then, the person doing the feeding always shut the gate behind him. None of the other sheep were getting out of the pen.

Then one day, Joe was going to the hen house to gather eggs when he saw Snowy standing by the gate to the sheep's pen. Joe stopped and hid around the corner. He watched Snowy. First, Snowy put a front hoof on a section of the gate. Then, he put the other

front hoof up, then his hind hooves, and finally, up and over he went! Snowy had climbed over the gate! Joe could not believe it. He ran to get Snowy just as he was starting to go out into the pasture. Joe's dad was close by and saw the whole thing, too. Joe grabbed the lamb and put him back into the sheep's pen.

"What will we do, Dad?" asked Joe.

"We will have to build the gate up higher," Dad said.

The next day, Joe helped Dad add another section to the gate so that it would be higher. Snowy never got out again.

1. How did Snowy get his name?
2. How was Snowy getting out of the sheep's pen?
3. How did Joe and his dad solve the problem?

The Science Class

Bill and Kurt were in science class together. They were doing an experiment. The teacher had said that they were to mix two liquids together and see what would happen.

Bill poured one of the liquids and Kurt poured the other. Bill stirred them together.

Kurt said, "What is that bad scent? It is awful!"

"Yes," said Bill. "That scent is the worst one I have ever smelled!"

Mr. Scripps, the science teacher, said, "That is because you have mixed cabbage water and salt water together. The cabbage water is what you are smelling."

"Well, it is bad!" said Bill.

"Take the dropper and add three drops of vinegar. See what happens," said Mr. Scripps.

Kurt put the three drops into the cabbage water. Bill and Kurt were surprised at what they saw.

"Hey! It turned green!" Bill cried.

"That is because the vinegar is an acid. The cabbage water turns green when it mixes with an acid," said Mr. Scripps.

"I am going to try this at home," said Kurt. "This was fun!"

"Just be careful. Vinegar can burn if you get it into your eyes. Make sure that you have a grown-up helping you," said Mr. Scripps.

"I will. Thanks, Mr. Scripps," said Kurt.

1. What were Bill and Kurt doing in science class?
2. Why was there a bad scent?
3. Why did the cabbage water turn green?

Jan's Wheel

Jan was riding her bike when the wheel came off. She fell down hard. She was not hurt badly, but she did not know why the wheel had come off.

She went and got Dad. She showed him her bike and the wheel that had come off.

Dad said, "The bolt must have come loose. I will fix it."

Later, Jan was riding her bike. The wheel came off again. Jan was getting upset now. She was afraid that her bike was no good anymore. She showed Dad what had happened.

"Okay," Dad said, "I think that it needs a new bolt. I will put a new one on. I do not know why the other one was not working."

"I am glad that my bike is still good. I was afraid that it was not," Jan said as she climbed on her bike. "Thanks, Dad."

"Where are you going?" Dad asked Jan.

"I am going to ride over to the park," said Jan. "Now I know that my bike is going to be all right."

1. What happened to Jan's bike?
2. What was wrong with the bike?
3. What did Dad do to fix the bike?

The Wrong Present

Mom was wrapping Christmas presents. There were many presents to wrap. Mom was writing tags for each present as she went.

Mom was almost finished wrapping a present when Jean came into the room. Mom had to hide the present quickly. After Jean left, Mom finished wrapping the present. She was not sure whose present it was. She thought it was Jean's, so she wrote  a tag with Jean's name on it and taped it to the present.

On Christmas morning, Jean and John were opening their presents. It was so much fun. Wrapping paper was all over the place! At last, there was one more present to unwrap! Jean took it because the tag had her name on it. She began unwrapping it. She got a funny look on her face.

"Mom," Jean said, "what is this?"

"Why Jean, that is John's! I do not think that you want a boy's shirt, do you?" Mom asked.

Jean laughed too. "Mom, what happened?"

"Well, this must have been the present that I was wrapping when you came into the room. I put the wrong tag on it!" Mom laughed.

Everyone thought that this was funny, even John. Jean gave the present to him to finish unwrapping.

When John took the shirt out of the box, Jean laughed and said, "I think that I do like that shirt! Can we share, John?"

Everyone laughed at that. It became a joke in their family for a long time.

1. What was Mom doing?
2. What went wrong?
3. Was John upset?
4. How did the family feel about what had happened?

The Wrong Sign

Mark was going to his friend Jim's house. His dad was driving him there. They were looking for Maple Street, which was the street where Jim lived. They had been following the map that Jim had given to Mark, but they could not find Maple Street.

Dad asked, "Are you sure that I was to turn right back there?"

Mark said, "Yes, I am. Maple Street should have been one street back."

"We will need to find a phone and call Jim," said Dad.

They stopped at a store to use the pay phone. Mark asked Jim if he and his dad were going the right way.

"Yes, you are doing fine," said Jim. "It sounds like you

passed Maple Street, so go back to it and you will be here."

"Okay," said Mark. "We will be there soon."

When they went back, the street sign said Elm Street, not Maple Street.

Dad said, "We will go around the other way and try it. We will try going to the end of the street and coming the other way."

When they got to the other end of the street, the sign said Maple Street.

"What happened?" said Mark. "Why does the sign at the other end of the street say Elm Street?"

"The sign must be wrong," Dad said.

When they got to Jim's house, sure enough, the sign had been wrong.

"I am sorry," Jim said. "I forgot to tell you about that sign. A new one was put up because the old one blew down in a storm. The new sign had the wrong street name."

Mark's dad laughed, "I was starting to think that I was seeing things!"

Jim said, "Next time you come over, I will remember to tell you to look for Elm and Maple Streets!"

1. What street were Mark and his dad looking for?
2. Why could they not find it?
3. What was wrong with the sign?

The Fox in the Box

Mike and his family went on a camping trip to the woods. When they got to the right spot, they put up the tent and got the food out of the car. They left the box that the tent had been in next to the tent. Then, they went for a hike.

They had a good time on the hike. They saw a rabbit and some deer. They saw wild flowers but did not pick them. They sat down to rest by a small stream.

When Mike and his family got back to their camp, they all went into the tent to take a nap. Mike was almost asleep when he heard a scratching noise. Then, it stopped. It began again a few minutes later. Mike woke up his dad.

Mike and Dad went outside to see what the noise was.

They could not find where the noise was coming from. They looked by the car and by a tree that was close to the camp. They went back to the tent. Then, they heard it again.

Dad said, "It sounds like it is coming from the box that the tent was in. Let's look in there."

Mike went to lift the box up, when a small, red fox jumped out! Mike and his dad were so surprised, that they both let out a yell! The fox ran off into the woods before they could get a good look at it.

"Wow, that was odd!" said Mike.

"Yes, I did not know that we would see a wild animal so close to our camp," Dad said.

They woke Mom and Mike's sister, Mary, up to tell them what had happened.

Mom said, "Well, we have had our fun for the day! What will happen tomorrow?"

1. What did Mike and his family do when they got to camp?
2. What odd thing did Mike and his dad find in the box?
3. What happened when they found it?

Fred's Lesson

Fred wanted to learn to play the xylophone. He thought it was the most fun musical instrument that he had ever seen. His mother did not know why Fred wanted to learn to play the xylophone. She wanted him to learn to play the trumpet or the clarinet. Those were much smaller instruments and would not take up so much space in Fred's room.

Fred had a hard time finding anyone who could give him xylophone lessons. He called the music store that was close to his house, but the people there did not know of anyone who gave xylophone lessons. He tried calling the office of the symphony in his town, but no one there knew of anyone either. Finally, Fred looked in the newspaper and saw an ad for music lessons. The ad said, "Music lessons given to children. I teach all instruments." Fred called the phone number in the ad.

"I would like to learn to play the xylophone," he said to the man who answered the phone.

"How old are you?" the man asked.

"I am ten years old," Fred said.

"All right. You may come to my house on Tuesday afternoon. I will give you xylophone lessons," the man said.

After Fred's mother had talked to the man and made sure that it was all right, she signed him up. She drove him over to the man's house that Tuesday night.

The man, whose name was Mr. Trask, had many musical instruments in his house. He knew how to play all of them. He had a very nice xylophone.

"Are you ready to start?" Mr. Trask asked.

"Yes! I can't wait!" Fred said. He was excited.

Fred had so much fun at his first lesson that he wanted to keep playing. He practiced every day after school. Mr. Trask was proud of Fred. He was a good student.

1. How did Fred find someone to give him lessons?

2. Where did Fred go for his lessons?

3. Did Fred like his lessons?

Jim Didn't Want To Go

Jim's friend Jay asked him to come to his birthday party. Jim had just moved into town and didn't know many kids. Jay and Jim went to the same church.

As the day of the party got closer, Jim didn't want to go. He was afraid because he wouldn't know any of the kids at the party.

Jim's mom said, "Don't be afraid. You will make friends. You will have fun."

Jim called Jay on the phone. He wanted to know who would be coming to the party.

Jay said, "There will be Jen, Mary, Mark, Greg and Tony."

Jim didn't know any of those kids. He wasn't sure at all about going to the party.

Jay said, "Just come anyway. You'll make friends. They are nice kids."

Jim said, "Okay, I'll try it."

On the day of the party, Jim's mom drove him to Jay's house. She said good-bye to him at the door. Jay let Jim in the house. As Jim went in, he saw all of the other kids. He got scared. He didn't want to stay.

Jay said, "This is my friend, Jim. We go to the same church."

All of the other kids said hello to Jim. Then Jay's

mom came in and took them all outside to play in the yard. They played some fun games and had birthday cake and milk. Then they saw Jay open his presents.

When Jim's mom came to get him she asked, "Well, did you have fun?"

"Oh, yes," said Jim. "I had a great time!"

Jim said thank you to Jay's mom. As he and his mom were going home, Jim said, "I can't believe that I was afraid to go to the party. I would have missed a good time if I hadn't gone."

1. Why didn't Jim want to go to the party?
2. What did Jay, Jim, and the rest of the kids do at the party?
3. How did Jim feel at the end of the story?

The Fair

Mary and her friend, Walt, went to the fair. They rode on the rides and ate cotton candy.

Mary said, "We'll have fun if we go see the animals."

Walt said, "Yes, they'll be fun to see."

Mary and Walt went over to the barn to see the cows and the goats that were at the fair. They were in pens in the barn.

Mary said, "I'll bet that these animals want to get out."

Walt said, "Look at this goat. He'll be glad to get out of here."

A man standing by the cows said, "We take good care of these cows. They give very good milk. Would you like to try a glass of fresh milk?"

Mary said, "Oh yes! But I would only like half a glass."

The milk was warm and fresh and tasted very good. Walt and Mary had never had fresh milk like that before.

As they left the barn, Mary said, "We'll be sure to come back to the fair next year."

Walt said, "Yes, I'll go with you."

1. What did Mary and Walt do at the fair?
2. What did the man tell Mary and Walt about the cows?
3. What do you like to do at the fair?

Mike Won't Come In

Mike liked to play outside. He played games with his friends and rode his bike. He was outside every day after school. His mom would call him to come in when it was time to eat supper.

One day, Mike was having a lot of fun outside. He was riding his bike and having races with his friends. He could see that it was getting dark, but he didn't want to go in. When Mom called him, he acted as if he didn't hear her.

Mom called, "Mike! Please come in now!"

Mike still rode his bike, just as if he hadn't heard her. He wasn't thinking that he might get in trouble and wouldn't get to go out the next day. He just kept riding and playing. Soon, Mom was getting upset.

Mom said to Dad, "Mike won't come in. He won't get to go out tomorrow."

Dad said, "He won't be happy about that. He shouldn't have stayed out when he was told to come in."

Mom went out and got Mike. She wasn't happy. She said, "Mike, I know that you could hear me calling you to come in. Now you'll have to stay in tomorrow."

Mike went in the house and to his room. He knew that he hadn't done the right thing by not coming in when Mom called him.

Mike came out of his room. He told Mom, "I am sorry that I didn't come in when you called me. I won't do that again."

Mom said, "I am sure that you'll do fine next time."

1. What did Mike like to do outside?
2. What did Mike do that was wrong?
3. What happened when Mike did the wrong thing?

They've Gone Away

Tom had a big tree in his front yard. The tree was very old. Many animals had lived in the tree over the years. One day, Tom saw a nest in the tree.

The nest was high up in the tree. It was too high for Tom to go up there. It wouldn't be safe. Tom wanted to know what was in the nest. He asked his friend, Dave.

"What do you think is in the nest?" Tom asked Dave.

"I don't know. I don't see any birds from here," said Dave.

"I wish that I could see what is in there," Tom said.

"Do you have a ladder? We could go up and look," said Dave. "Yes, I have a ladder. But, my dad said that I wasn't to use it by myself," said Tom. "Let's do it when my dad is home. He can help us."

The next day, Tom and Dave asked Tom's dad to use the ladder to go up into the tree and look at the nest.

Tom's dad said, "There are three baby birds in here. I will come down and you can come up and look."

Tom went up first. He saw the baby birds. They were just sitting there looking at him. Dave went up next. He also saw the birds.

When he came down, he said, "They look big enough to fly. I'll bet that the mother bird is out getting food for them."

"Yes, that is what mother birds do," said Tom's dad. "We'll check on them tomorrow."

The next day, Tom's dad went up the ladder to look at the birds. He had a funny look on his face.

"Boys, I'm afraid that the birds are gone. They must have flown away," Tom's dad said.

Dave said, "Well, they did look big enough. I wish them well!"

"Me too," Tom said. "Maybe there will be some other birds in our tree again."

1. What did Tom and Dave see in the tree?
2. How did they get up in the tree to look?
3. What did Tom's dad think happened to the birds?

It's A Nice Day

Mark and Lori are friends. They like to go places together. They play together.

One day, Mark said, "I think that it's going to be a nice day."

"Why do you think so?" asked Lori.

"It's sunny and warm. We can go to the park," said Mark.

"I'll ask my mom if I can go," said Lori.

Mark said, "Let's ask Marge if she can go. She's our friend, too."

Lori asked her mom if she could go to the park. Mom said, "I'll take you and your friends to the park. You can have fun there."

Lori's mom drove Lori, Mark, and Marge to the park. They played a game of tag. Then they played hide-and-seek. Lori was the first one to be "it". She found Marge, but she couldn't find Mark.

After some time, she called his name. Marge said, "He's over there!" She pointed to the picnic table. Mark was hiding behind it.

Lori called, "I see you, Mark! Come out!"

Mark ran over to the girls. It was Marge's turn to be "it". They played for a while longer, then Lori's mom said that it was time to go home.

Mark said, "It's been a nice day. I've had a great time!"

Lori said, "Maybe we can do this again some other time."

1. Why did Mark think that it was going to be a nice day?
2. Who did Lori and Mark take with them to the park?
3. What games did they play at the park?

She's A Good Dog

Sally had a dog. The dog's name was Kit. Kit was a good dog. She could do many tricks. Sally's friends liked to see Kit do her tricks. She could catch a ball with her teeth. She could roll over and lie on her back.

Sally and Kit played in Sally's yard. Sally threw the ball to Kit and Kit caught it. They did this a lot. Then, Sally saw Kit stop playing. She was looking at something. Sally could not see what she was looking at. Kit sat there for some time. Then she ran across the street. Kit stopped by some bushes in front of a house.

Sally went over to where Kit was sitting. She didn't see anything. Kit was still sitting there. Then Sally could hear a little sound. It was like a squeak. It was very low. More things began to make the sound. Kit got up and began to look in the bushes. Sally looked too. She saw three little kittens in the bushes. They were making the sound! Sally got the three kittens and went up to the door of the house. She knocked on the door. A lady opened the door.

Sally asked, "Are these your kittens?"

"Why, yes they are," said the lady. "We have been looking all over for them. Where did you find them?"

"My dog found them in your bushes," said Sally.

"My goodness! I don't know how they got there," said the lady.

"My dog found them. She could hear them crying and ran over," said Sally.

"Well, you have a very good dog," said the lady.

"Yes, she's a very good dog," said Sally.

1. What tricks did Kit do?
2. Why did Kit run across the street?
3. What did Kit and Sally find?

I'm Playing

Julie had a little brother named James. James was two years old. He liked to play. He liked to play with Julie. They played with blocks and with cars. They liked to play outside.

Julie was teaching James how to talk. James was a good learner. He was saying "mama" and "daddy" and "cookie."

Sometimes, Julie liked to play by herself in her room. She played with her dolls. She didn't want James in her room because he made a mess of her dolls. She would tell him, "I'm playing, James."

One day, James was playing with his cars. He was sitting in his room. Mom was looking in on him to make sure that he was okay. Then, Julie came in. She wanted to play cars with James.

"May I play cars with you, James?" Julie asked.

James looked at her. He had a funny look on his face. He said, "I'm playing."

Julie stopped and looked at James. He had not said that before. Mom started to laugh.

"Julie, that is what you say to him," Mom said.

"Yes, I know. It is funny! He must have learned to say that from me," Julie said.

James looked at Julie and again said, "I'm playing."

Mom said, "I guess that this means he doesn't want us in here!"

Julie and her mom let James play by himself, but looked in on him to make sure that he was okay. Julie decided that she would try letting him play with her dolls.

1. What did James and Julie like to do together?
2. What did Julie like to do by herself?
3. What funny thing did James say?
4. What did Julie decide to do?

The Spring Dress

Joan had a dress that she really loved. It was her new spring dress. The dress was purple, with white flowers splashed all over it. It had a little apron that went over it. It tied in the back.

Joan's mom didn't want her to wear the dress to

school. She was afraid that Joan might get it dirty or rip it. She wanted Joan to wear it only to church. Joan didn't like that. She loved the dress so much that she wanted  to wear it everywhere, even to the store.

One Monday morning, when Joan was getting ready for school, she took out her spring dress. She looked at it and wanted so much to wear it that day. She knew that her mom didn't want her to. She thought that if she wore her long coat over the dress, Mom wouldn't know that she had it on. She put it on. She got her long coat and put it on over the dress.

Mom called, "Joan, are you ready to go?"

"Yes, Mom!" Joan called.

Joan went down the hall and gave her mom a kiss and a hug good-bye. Mom didn't say anything about the dress. Maybe she hadn't seen it.

Joan got to school. Everything was going fine. When it was time for recess, she ran out to the playground. As she was running, she didn't see a tree root and fell over it. The dress tore in the back, near the tie. Joan was scared. She felt sick.

"Oh, no," she thought. "I shouldn't have worn this dress after all. My mom will not like this."

Her teacher gave her some pins to fix the rip. This helped a little bit. Still, she knew that she would have to tell her mom when she got home.

When Joan got home, she went to her room and took off the dress. She tried to think about what to say to her mom. She knew she had to tell Mom the truth. She put on a shirt and pants and went to her mom.

Joan said, "Mom, I know that you didn't want me to wear my new spring dress to school. I'm sorry to say that I did wear it today, and I tore it."

Mom said, "I know that you wore the dress. I saw it under your coat. I am sorry that you tore the dress. We will see if we can fix it."

Joan felt very sorry. She got the dress and took it to Mom.

Mom said, "I think that I can fix this, but it won't look the same as it did before. Now do you know why I didn't want you to wear it to school?"

"Yes, I do. I have learned a lesson this time. Thanks, Mom," said Joan.

1. Where did Joan want to wear her spring dress?
2. Where did Mom allow Joan to wear her dress?
3. What happened when Joan wore the dress to school?
4. What did Mom do?

Steph Didn't Stay

Steph wanted to go to camp. She liked to be outside and hike. She liked to be with other kids. She had wanted to go to camp for a long time. Her mom said that it was okay. She could go in the summer when there wasn't any school.

Steph took a bus to the camp. It was a camp just for girls. There would be swimming and fishing and hiking. They would be sleeping in cabins. Steph knew that she would have fun.

The first day of camp, the girls all met each other and had lunch. Then, the camp leaders took the girls on a hike. It was fun. They hiked in the woods. Then, they came back to camp and had supper. After supper, they made a campfire and sang songs. Soon, it was time to go to bed. All of the girls went to their cabins.

Steph wasn't feeling good. She felt scared. She wanted to go home. She missed her mom and dad. She missed her bedroom and her toys. She felt bad. She went to one of the camp leaders and told her about it.

The leader said, "Maybe you would like to go home."

Steph said, "Yes, I think I would. I didn't think that I

would feel this way, but I miss my mom and dad."

"We will call them. They will have to come and get you," the leader said.

The leader called Steph's mom and dad on the phone. Mom said, "We'll come and get her. I'll bet that she's scared."

"Yes, it's too bad that she didn't want to stay," said the leader.

"Well, we'll be there soon," Mom said.

When her mom and dad got there, Steph was very glad to see them.

1. What did Steph and the other girls do the first day of camp?
2. What happened to Steph the first night of camp?
3. How did Steph feel at the end of the story?

The Twins

Twila and Travis are twins. They were born at the same time. They both have red hair and freckles. They like to do lots of the same things.

Travis likes to go swimming. So does Twila. Twila likes to ride bikes. So does Travis.

Twila and Travis both like to go to the toy store in town. They look at all of the toys. Twila likes the dolls. Travis likes to look at the toy animals.

They also like to go to the snack shop. There are many good things to eat in there. Twila likes the candy cane twist. Travis does too. It comes in twenty flavors.

152

The other store the twins like to visit is the sports shop. This store has balls, bats, mitts, and all kinds of other things that are needed to play sports. The store even has swimming gear. One time, the twins got swim fins and swimming suits there.

Twila and Travis are glad that, even though they are twins, their mom does not make them dress alike.

"I sure would look silly in a dress," joked Travis.

1. What do Twila and Travis like in the toy store?
2. What candy does Twila and Travis like?
3. Why do Twila and Travis like to go to the sports shop?

The Kitten Who Wouldn't Come Down

Mary and her friends were in her yard. They were looking up in the tree. There was a kitten in the tree. It wouldn't come down. The kitten had gotten up in the tree, but it didn't know how to get down.

Mary's friend Joe came over. He was an older boy. He wanted to help get the kitten down from the tree.

Joe said, "I'll go home and get my ladder. I will go up there and get the kitten down."

Joe went home and came back with a ladder.

He climbed up and tried to get the kitten. When he put his arms out, the kitten just went up and up. Joe couldn't reach it. He went down the ladder and let it out some more so that it was higher. He went back up. He got up to the kitten and tried to get it. This time, the kitten didn't move. Joe could get the kitten. All of the kids were happy.

The kitten belonged to Mary's friend, Kathy. Kathy said thank you to Joe and took her kitten home.

Mary said, "I'll bet that kitten won't try that again!"

Joe said, "Let's hope not!"

1. How was the kitten in trouble?
2. How did Joe save the kitten?
3. What did Kathy do with her kitten?

The Baseball Team

Matt was on a baseball team. The team was called the Tigers. They were a good team. They won a lot of their games. They  played their games at the field by the railroad tracks.

Matt kept all of his baseball things in a backpack. He had a mitt and a bat and a ball. He liked to play baseball very much. It was fun.

A lot of people came to watch their games. The people would eat popcorn or peanuts as they watched the game. One boy even had a cupcake at one of the games.

Matt played in the outfield. His job was to try to catch the ball after the batter had hit it. He had to throw the ball to the person closest to him. He was a good catcher and a good thrower. He helped the boys on the team to win their games.

Matt liked baseball so much that he wanted to be a baseball player when he was grown up.

1. Where did Matt's team play its games?
2. What did the people eat at the games?
3. What was Matt's job on the team?
4. What did Matt want to be when he was grown up?

The Buzzing Bees

Jen had a beehive in a tree on the side of her house. She liked to look at the hive and the bees that were buzzing around it. She tried not to get too close to it, because she didn't want to get stung. Jen knew that the hive was bad to have near a house. She liked looking at it so much that she didn't tell her mom and dad about it.

Jen went to the hive every day to see what was going on. The bees were buzzing around. They were going out and getting nectar from the flowers. Then, they came back to the hive. It was fun to watch them.

One day, Jen's mom was in her garden. She was picking flowers and pulling weeds. She could hear a buzzing sound. It was coming from the tree. She stopped and looked. As she went closer to the tree,

the sound got louder. As she looked up into the tree, she saw a beehive. She backed up slowly and went inside. She went and got Jen.

"Jen," Mom said, "there is a beehive in our tree. Don't go out there until we get rid of it."

Jen felt bad. She didn't think about her mom getting hurt, but she could have.

"Mom, I know that the hive is there," Jen said. "I saw it a few weeks ago."

"Jen, you should've told me. Someone could've gotten hurt." Mom said.

"Yes, Mom," Jen said.

Even if she was sad, Jen knew that it was for the best.

"I'm sorry. I didn't think about that," Jen said. "I just liked watching the bees."

"I understand," said Mom. "But we'll have to get rid of it before someone gets hurt."

1. What did the bees do?
2. Why did Jen and her mom need to get rid of the hive?
3. How did Jen feel at the end of the story?

Max Painted a Picture

Max wanted to paint a picture. He got out his paints and a cup of water. He got some paper out of his paper box. He thought about what he wanted to paint. First, he painted a big, blue sky. Then, he painted some trees and grass. He liked animals, so he painted some cows and a dog. The dog's job was to guard the cows from wolves or other animals that might want to get them. He painted a white farmhouse. A family lived there. The family had a mom and a dad and a boy and a girl. He painted them all next to the farmhouse.

Max's mom came in the room and looked at his picture. She said, "Max, that is very good. I like it. May I have it when you are done?"

"Sure, Mom," Max said. "I will make the picture very nice for you."

Max had more room on the paper, so he painted some flowers by the house. He painted a red barn and a white fence around the house. Then, his picture was done.

"Mom!" he called. "I'm done with the picture!"

Mom came in and looked at it again. "Why, that is so good! I am glad to have it," Mom said. "Thank you for giving it to me."

Mom gave Max a big hug and hung the picture on the kitchen wall.

1. What did Max paint in his picture?
2. What was the dog's job?
3. What did Mom do with the picture?

The Cat Who Jumps

Sam is a cat who likes to jump. He jumps in his house.
He jumps outside. He jumps whenever someone pets
him. He jumps to show that he is happy.

Tom is Sam's owner. Tom thinks that Sam's jumping is
funny. He doesn't know where Sam learned to jump.
One day, Sam just started doing it. When Tom feeds
him, Sam jumps. Tom thinks that Sam is saying, "Thanks
for the food." Sam also jumps whenever Tom lets him

outside. He seems glad to be out. Tom goes out and plays with him. Tom also brushes Sam. The only time that Sam doesn't jump is when Tom brushes him. Then, he sits and purrs.

Tom's friends like to see Sam jump. They think that it is funny. They play outside with him. He jumps and jumps! Sometimes, he runs to  school with Tom as he walks with his friends. Everyone loves Sam, the jumping cat.

1. Why does Sam jump?
2. What else does Sam sometimes do when Tom walks to school with his friends?
3. Would you like a jumping cat? Why or why not?

The Helpful Friend

Janet was a helpful friend. She was always there when her friends needed her. She knew just how to make a sick friend feel better. She would help out if someone needed help.

Once, her friend Grace was sick. She had a cold and couldn't come to school. Janet and Grace were in the same class, so Janet got  Grace's work for her. She took the work to Grace and helped her with it. She got Grace some juice and soup that Grace's mom had made for her. She stayed with her and helped to make Grace feel better.

Another time, Janet's friend, Marsha, got hurt when

she was riding her bike. Janet was careful not to move her. Janet called Marsha's mom and dad on the phone and stayed with Marsha until they got there to take her home.

Janet had a lot of friends that she liked to help. They helped her, too. When Janet had a sore throat, her friend Grace remembered how Janet had helped her. She came over to make her feel better.

Janet knows that friends are helpful to each other. She is a good friend.

1. How did Janet help Grace?
2. How did Janet help Marsha?
3. What would be another way to help a friend?

The Careless Boy

Jack was a careless boy. He did things that sometimes hurt people, and he wouldn't even know it. Sometimes, he caused sadness because he was careless.

One time, Jack was playing catch with his friend, Tim. Jack wasn't looking where he was throwing, and he hit Tim hard in the arm. Tim was upset with Jack because Jack had been careless. Jack said, "I'm sorry, Tim. I didn't mean to hurt you."

"Okay, but next time, look where you are throwing the ball," said Tim.

Another time, Jack was playing with his little sister, Tina. She was just starting to walk. Jack didn't look out for her and she fell over his foot. Tina cried. Jack felt very badly. Mom said, "You need to be more careful with your sister."

From then on, Jack told himself that he would stop being so careless. He was hopeful that he could do it.

1. How was Jack careless with his friend, Tim?

2. How was Jack careless with his sister?

3. Do you think that Jack will stop being careless? Why or why not?

Riding Safely

It is good to ride your bike safely. Getting hurt, it isn't any fun. You need to wear a helmet at all times. You could fall suddenly, and if you weren't wearing a helmet, you could hurt your head badly.

It is also a good idea to wear kneepads and elbow pads, so that if you fall, you won't hurt your knees and elbows.

When you first start riding, it is good to ride slowly and take it easy. You need to learn how to balance before you start to go fast.

If you want to ride at night, you should have a light on your bike. That way, cars can see you. You should also have an adult ride with you at night. That is the safe way to ride at night.

If you ride your bike safely, you'll have more fun. Remember to follow all of the rules, and you'll have a good time.

1. What should you wear when you ride your bike?
2. Why should you wear these things?
3. What do you need to have to ride at night?

The Wooden Box

Gail had a wooden box. Her grandma had given it to her for her fourth birthday. The box was made of dark wood and could hold many things.

The box had golden paint on the lid. The paint had seemed to darken over the years. That made it look nicer, Gail thought. The box had red velvet inside.
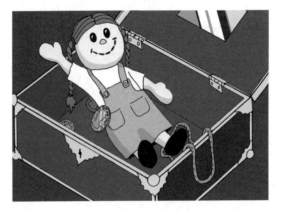
It had seemed to soften over time.

Gail liked to put things in her box. She put money, toys, and jewelry in the box. She had a golden necklace that she kept in the box. She put a little doll in the box. She also kept all of her money in there for safekeeping.

Gail didn't let anyone know where she kept the box. She kept it hidden in her desk. She was frightened that someone would take it. Her mom told her not to get upset about it.

Mom said, "We all know that the box is yours. No one will take it."

Gail said, "Okay. I will keep my box out."

Mom said, "Yes, because we all like to look at it."

From then on, Gail kept the box out for all of her family to see.

1. What did Gail's box look like?
2. What did Gail keep in the box?
3. What was Gail frightened of?

The Deeper Hole

Chester had a dog named Rocky. Rocky loved to dig holes. He dug wherever he could. The place that he liked the best was Chester's yard.

Chester's mom had told him not to let Rocky dig holes. She didn't like having holes in the yard. If Rocky dug a hole, she would have to fill it in. It was a lot of work.

One day, Rocky got out of the house without anyone knowing it. He wanted to dig. It had just rained, so the dirt was softer than before. Rocky ran out in the yard. The dirt was good for digging. He dug and he dug. He dug a deeper hole than he had ever dug before.

He was tired when he was done, so he lay down in the grass to rest.

Chester went out the front door to get the mail. He saw Rocky sleeping in the grass. "Hey, what are you doing here?" Chester asked. "You should be in the house. It is too muddy for you to be out here."

Just then, Chester saw the hole that Rocky had dug. Rocky woke up and looked at him. "Oh, no," Chester said. "Now, I'll have to fill this in before Mom sees it."

Chester got the shovel. He began to fill in the hole. It was hard work. He could see why Mom didn't want

Rocky to dig in the yard. Mom looked out of the window and saw them.

She opened the window and said, "Now, you see what I mean."

"Yes, I do. From now on, I will make sure that he doesn't dig in the yard," Chester said.

1. Where did Rocky like to dig?
2. Why did Mom not want Rocky to dig there?
3. Do you think that Rocky will dig again? Why or why not?

The Happier Day

Joan was not having a good day. She got up late in the morning, and was late for school. It was rainier than it had been all week. She got wet and cold walking to school.

When she got to school, her friend, Sarah, was being sillier than she had been for a long time. Sarah tried to make jokes, but Joan just said, "You'll have to tell sillier ones than that. I am not in a good mood."

Because it was raining, the kids couldn't go outside. It was no fun. Joan wished that they could go home earlier. The day seemed to go on forever.

When school was over, Joan and Sarah walked home

in the rain. Sarah stayed at Joan's house to see if she could make her happier.

Joan's mom said, "I wish that the day were sunnier, too. Please stop being so grumpy."

Joan said, "I'll try. Maybe if Sarah stays for supper, I'll feel better."

Sarah called her mom, who said that it was all right for Sarah to stay. By the time supper was over, Joan was feeling much better.

Joan said, "Maybe tomorrow will be sunnier. I will be happier then."

1. Why was Joan having a bad day?
2. What did Sarah do to try to make Joan feel better?
3. What did Joan hope for?

The Darkest Room

Linda didn't like to go into the room at the end of the hallway. It was very dark. She thought that it was the darkest room in the house.

Sometimes, she had to go in there to help her mom clean the house. It was Linda's job to do the dusting. Even if the room didn't get used very much, it still had to be dusted. Because it wasn't used very much, this scared Linda even more.

She thought that she could hear things coming from the room. Mom would tell her that it was just the wind, or that the window had a loose screen. She wanted to believe her mom.

At night, the room was the darkest room because it didn't have a lamp in it. Linda wouldn't go in there at night. Her dad told her that was silly. He said, "We'll go in there together. I will take a lamp and you will see that there is no need to be scared."

Linda and her dad went into the darkest room. Dad turned on the lamp. There were just a lot of things in there that the family didn't use much anymore.

"See? There is nothing to be scared of," Dad said.

"Okay, but could we keep a lamp in here so that I can turn on the light and then I won't be scared?" asked Linda.

"Sure," said Dad. "Maybe we can make this into a play room for you!"

"That's a great idea, Dad," said Linda. "That will put this room to good use, and I won't be scared anymore!"

1. Why didn't Linda like the room at the end of the hall?
2. How did Dad stop Linda from being scared of the room?
3. What did Dad say that he would do with the room?

The Funniest Clown

Jill liked to go to the circus. She loved the clowns. There was one clown that she really liked. She thought he was the best.

The clown had orange hair and big feet. He had a red nose and red cheeks. He ran around the circus ring, acting silly. Jill thought that was so funny!

The clowns had an act in which they threw balls to each other. At first, they all caught the balls. Then, they started to miss them. Soon, they weren't catching any of the balls. Jill laughed and laughed. The clown that Jill liked the best was the silliest. He also seemed to be the happiest clown.

Another act that the clowns had was one in which they used the dogs. There were three little dogs that were so funny! They chased the clowns, and the clowns chased them. The little dogs caught balls in their mouths

that the clowns threw to them. The dogs wore little hats on their heads. Jill's favorite clown was the funniest one. At one time, all of the dogs were chasing him. That was the funniest thing of all!

Jill always had the best time at the circus. She felt like she was the happiest kid in the world!

1. What did Jill's favorite clown look like?
2. What did the clowns do in their acts?
3. What did the little dogs do in the clown acts?

Luke and Sue

Luke and Sue were friends. They were in the same second grade class at school. They even lived near each other. They also liked to play music. Luke played the tuba, and Sue played the flute.

Sometimes, Luke and Sue would visit each other's house and play music together. Their instruments sounded very different. Luke's tuba played low notes. Sue's flute played high notes. They laughed together when they made funny sounds.

One day, Sue said, "Let's have a concert for our parents. We could learn some songs and play together."

Luke said, "That is a great idea. We'll ask Mrs. Clark for some songs that we could play together."

The next day, Luke and Sue asked Mrs. Clark, their music teacher, for some songs that a tuba and a flute could play together. Mrs. Clark had three songs that they could play together. Luke and Sue ran home after school to practice.

They practiced at Luke's house, since his parents were still at work. His big brother Mike was there.

Luke and Sue wanted the concert to be a surprise for their parents. They practiced at Luke's house every day after school for a week. By the end of the week, they felt like they were ready to give their concert for their parents.

That Friday, Luke asked his parents if they could have Sue and her parents over for dinner on Saturday night.

Luke's mom said, "That would be fun. We haven't seen them in a long time."

After dinner that night, Luke and Sue brought their parents into the living room. They told them that they had a surprise for them.  Then, Luke and Sue got their flute and tuba from Luke's room. They played the three songs for their surprised parents. The parents clapped and cheered after each song. They all had a wonderful time!

Sue's dad said, "We didn't know that you two had been playing together. You did a very good job!"

Luke's mom said, "Yes. We are very surprised and happy that you two enjoy playing your tuba and flute so much."

Luke and Sue looked at each other with cute smiles. They both agreed that they would keep playing the tuba and the flute together.

1. What instrument did Luke play? What did Sue play?
2. What did they plan for their parents?
3. What did Luke and Sue agree to do at the end of the story?

The Purple Candies

Ted went to the store to get some candy. His mom took him because he had been good and done all of his work at home. He wanted to get some purple candies.

Ted saw the candies that he wanted. They were hard candies. He had enough money to get five candies. They were one penny each. He took them off of the shelf. He took them to the man at the counter. He gave the man five pennies. The man put the candies into a bag. Ted thanked the man and left with his mom.

When they got home, Ted took one of the candies out of the bag. He thought that he'd eat one then, and have one after supper. He would save the rest until the next day. The next morning, he got into his candy bag. He should've had three candies. He had only two. He was sure that he'd only had two the day before. He thought maybe his sister had taken one. He went to her room.

"Have you taken one of my candies?" Ted asked his sister.

"No, I don't like purple candies. I only like candy cherries. I didn't take your candy," Amanda said.

He asked his mom. Mom said, "I don't know who could've taken your candy. Did you leave the bag on the floor?

"I think that I did," said Ted. "I should have been more careful and put it on my desk. Who do you think got the candy?"

"Maybe it was Ginger," said Mom.

Ginger was their dog. Surely, she didn't like purple candies. Ted went and looked at Ginger's lips. They were purple! She was the one!

Ted thought, "I wonder why she ate only one candy. Next time, I will be more careful!"

1. Why did Ted get the candies?
2. What happened to the missing candy?
3. What will Ted do next time?

The Fluffiest Bunnies

Kate went to the pet store. She liked to look at all of the animals. She really liked the bunnies. The store had two white bunnies, three black bunnies, and four brown bunnies.

Kate thought the white ones were the fluffiest ones.

There was one white bunny that Kate really liked. It was soft with a pink nose. It hopped around a lot. Kate asked the lady who worked in the store if she could hold one of the white bunnies. The lady took one of them out of the cage that they were in. The lady said that children couldn't hold the animals but that she would hold the bunny and Kate could pet it.

Kate petted the bunny's soft fur. It was funny the way that the bunny moved its nose like it was sniffing the air. Kate asked how much this bunny would cost to buy. The lady said that the bunnies cost twenty-five dollars each. Kate thought that it was a lot of money. She could ask for it for her birthday. Her birthday was coming up in two weeks.

Kate thanked the lady and walked home. She told her mom about the bunny. She told her how it was the fluffiest bunny of all. She asked for it for her birthday. Her mom said that she would think about it.

The day of Kate's birthday came. Her mom and dad gave Kate her presents. She got a dress, some pants, a doll, and a game. She felt sad that she had not gotten the bunny.

Then, Dad said, "I think that we've left something out.

I'll be right back."

He came back with the white bunny in a little cage,
just like the bunny in the pet store. Kate was so happy! She took the bunny out of its cage and held it. She petted its soft fur. She said, "Thanks so much! This is the best present of all!"

She named the bunny Fluffy, of course.

1. What color were the bunnies in the pet store?
2. What did Kate like about the white bunnies?
3. What did Kate get for her birthday?
   What was her favorite present?

The Lonely Prince

Once, there was a prince who lived in a big house. The house was very pretty. The prince had many people taking care of him. He didn't have to cook, clean, or even wash his clothes. He had a mom and a dad (the king and queen) who loved him very much. Even with all of those things, the prince wasn't happy with his life.

One day, the prince was walking in the woods near his house. He met a little man with a cane. The little man's name was Len.

Len said, "What is wrong, my prince? You look sad."

"Who are you?" the prince asked.

"My name is Len. I have been watching you as you were walking. Why do you look so sad?"

"I am not happy with my life," the prince said.

"Well, why not? You have the best of everything! You should be the happiest person ever!" Len said.

"I need a friend. I don't have any friends who are my age. I have to stay at my house most of the time because the king and queen worry that something will happen to me," the prince said.

Ah, yes. Friends are very nice to have. I think that I can help you," Len told him.

He told the prince he would return the next day. When he came back, he had a boy with him the same age as the prince.

"Where did you find a friend for me?" the prince asked.

"This is my son," Len said. "I have many children who will be your friend. I am glad I can help you."

From that day on, the prince was happy, knowing that he had a friend who would help him.

1. Why was the prince sad?
2. How did Len help the prince?
3. What kind of adventures do you think Len and the prince will have together?

The Lemonade Stand

Paul wanted to make some money. He needed money to buy a new football. He told his mom that he needed to make some money. She gave him some ideas.

"You're going to have to work hard to get that much money. I've got some jobs for you to do," Mom said. "You can rake the leaves and set the table for supper every night this week."

"I'll do those jobs. They're not going to be too hard," said Paul.

Paul raked the leaves that day, and set the table every night. At the end of the week, Mom paid him for the jobs.

Paul said, "Thanks, Mom. I'm afraid I'll need more money than this to get the football. What else can I do?"

"Well, it's hot outside and people might want something to drink. Why don't you try to set up a lemonade stand?" Mom asked.

"Okay, that's a good idea," Paul said. He was excited. He got a table and some chairs out of the garage. He made a big sign that said, "Lemonade: 10 Cents a Cup." Mom helped him make a big jug of lemonade and gave him some plastic cups. He put some ice in a big ice chest and took everything outside to the curb in front of his house.

He sat for what seemed like a long time. He was getting hot himself. He had a cup of the lemonade. His friend Jason came by on his bike.

"Say, can I have a cup of lemonade? Jason asked.

"That will cost you 10 cents," Paul said.

Jason gave Paul a dime and drank his lemonade. Just as Jason was leaving, Mr. Smith, Paul's neighbor, stopped by in his car.

"That lemonade looks good. I'll take a cup," he said.

"Ten cents, please," Paul said.

Mr. Smith gave Paul the money and drank his lemonade. Pretty soon, Paul had five people waiting to get cups of lemonade. The lemonade stand was a good idea. Paul made enough money to buy the football, as well as a baseball that he wanted.

Paul told his mom, "That was a great idea! Next time I need some money, I'll be sure to come to you for more ideas."

1. What did Paul need money for?
2. What jobs did Mom give Paul to do?
3. How did Paul make the rest of the money?

Art Class

Gail liked art class at her school. She thought that it was a lot of fun. She liked art class because everyone got to use clay, paint, and paper. She liked making things.

Gail's favorite thing to work with was the clay. She and the kids in her class made pots out of the clay. Gail made a round pot. Some kids made their pots square or oval. Gail was going  to use her pot to keep her rings in. She would put it on her desk in her bedroom.

After the kids had made the pots, the art teacher put

the pots into a special oven, called a kiln. The kiln baked the pots so that the clay would get hard. When the pots were baked, Gail and the other kids painted the pots with a special paint, called

glaze. Gail painted her pot red and pink, her favorite colors. After the pots were painted, they went back into the kiln to be baked again. This made the paint hard and shiny.

All of the pots were very pretty. Gail loved hers. It would be just right for her rings.

Gail's friend, Kay, made a square pot. She painted it blue. Kay's pot was to go in the bathroom at her house. She would put extra soap in it.

When Gail got home with her pot, she showed her mom. Mom said, "That is so pretty! What will you do with it?"

"I am going to put my rings in it," said Gail.

"What a good idea! Maybe next time, you could make a pot for me," Mom said.

1. What did Gail like to do in art class?
2. What was Gail's favorite thing to do in art class?
3. What was Gail going to use her pot for?

The Teacher Reads A Book

Mrs. Reese was a first-grade teacher. She loved her students. She loved to read books to them. Every day, her students couldn't wait until it was time for her to read to them. She would read to them before they left for the day.

There were many books in the classroom. There were books about animals, people, and cities. There were storybooks and make-believe books. Mrs. Reese made sure that there were lots of books for her students to read.

All of the students agreed that their favorite book was "The Sleeping Town." It was about a town in which all of the people went to sleep and didn't wake up for awhile.

A little girl came to the town while they were asleep and lived in the town. She was afraid that the people wouldn't let her stay if they knew about her. She had fun living in the town.

One by one, the people woke up and found out that the girl was there. In the end, the people didn't mind that the girl lived there. One family even let her live in their house and she got to play with the children.

It was a happy story.

Mrs. Reese had read the story to the students so many times that most of them knew the words to the story and could say them with her. They had such fun doing it. She let her students feel free to read with her. They all agreed that reading was the most fun part of the day.

1. What kinds of books did Mrs. Reese have in the classroom?
2. What was the name of the students' favorite book?
3. What was the book about?

The Cherry Pie

Cara and her mom were going to make a cherry pie. It was Cara's favorite kind of pie. Cara had been waiting a long time for her mom to help her make it.

First, they made the crust. They used flour, shortening, and water. Cara mixed it all together, then used her hands to mix it when it got thick. She put flour on her hands so that the crust wouldn't stick to them. Then, Cara helped her mom roll out the crusts into two circles.

Cara put the circle of crust carefully into a pie plate and poured the cherry pie filling into the crust. Her mom helped her to put the second crust onto the top of the filling. Then, they pinched the edges of the crust together to seal it so that the filling wouldn't bubble out when it baked. Mom put the pie into the hot oven.

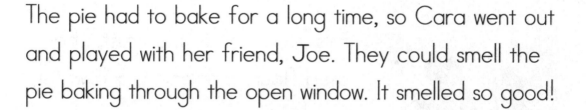

The pie had to bake for a long time, so Cara went out and played with her friend, Joe. They could smell the pie baking through the open window. It smelled so good!

After the pie had cooled off, Cara and Joe had a piece. Joe said, "This is the best pie I've ever eaten!"

Cara said, "Thanks. It was fun to make. Maybe next time you can help us."

1. What kind of pie did Cara make?
2. Why did Cara put flour on her hands?
3. What did Cara and Joe smell through the open window?

The Letter

Zoe wrote a letter to her grandma. She didn't get to see her grandma very much, and she missed her. She wanted to write the letter the correct way, so her mom helped her. She reminded Zoe about the five parts of a friendly letter: the heading, greeting, body, closing, and signature. Here is what Zoe's letter said:

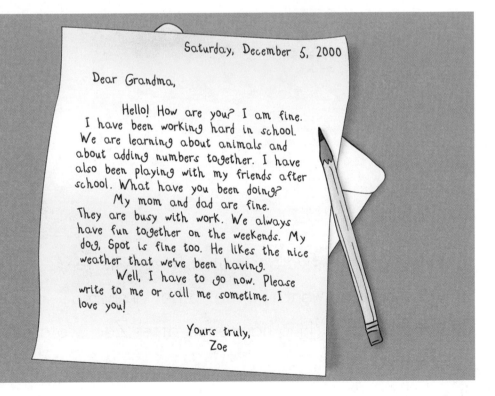

Saturday, December 5, 2000

Dear Grandma,

    Hello! How are you? I am fine. I have been working hard in school. We are learning about animals and about adding numbers together. I have also been playing with my friends after school. What have you been doing?

    My mom and dad are fine. They are busy with work. We always have fun together on the weekends. My dog, Spot is fine too. He likes the nice weather that we've been having.

    Well, I have to go now. Please write to me or call me sometime. I love you!

                Yours truly,
                Zoe

Zoe put a stamp on the letter and her mom mailed it for her. Zoe was happy when she got a letter back from her grandma a week later. Grandma said that she would be coming to visit soon. Zoe was very excited! She was glad that she had written the letter to her grandma.

1. What are the five parts of a friendly letter?
2. Why did Zoe want to write to her grandma?
3. What exciting thing happened after Zoe wrote to her grandma?

The Cool Pool

Jane wanted to go swimming. It had been a long winter and a cold spring. She wanted summer to come. The water had been taken out of her family's pool for the winter. Now it was starting to get warm. Her dad had filled the pool with water for the summer. Since it was in early May, it wasn't quite warm enough to go swimming.

Jane was so excited to have water in the pool. She looked at it every day. One day, she came home from school and was feeling hot. It had been a warm day. She wanted to go for a swim. She asked Mom, but Mom said no.

The water was still too cold for swimming. Jane went out and looked at the pool. The water looked so nice.

She wanted to jump right in. Then she remembered what her mom had said. She reached down and felt the water. It was very cold! She put her arm in a little more. The water cooled her arm. She put her arm in a little more, and then a little more. Before she knew it, she had lost her footing, and fallen in!

Jane yelled loudly because the water was so cold. Mom came running out of the house. "Jane!" Mom cried. "Are you all right?"

"Yes, Mom. I'm fine," Jane said as she got out of the pool. She was very wet.

"I told you not to go in the pool," Mom said.

"I didn't mean to go in," Jane said. "I put my arm in, and then I lost my footing and fell in."

"Well, you could have been hurt very badly," Mom said.

"From now on, I will stay away from the pool until the water is warm enough," said Jane.

"I hope so," said Mom. "I don't want you to get hurt."

1. Why couldn't Jane go in the pool?
2. What happened when Jane put her arm in the pool?
3. Do you think that Jane will do that again?
   Why or why not?

The Red Sweater

Dora had a red sweater. She had gotten it for her birthday the year before. It was warm and cozy. She liked to wear it on cold winter days. She wore it to school and when she went sledding with her friends.

The sweater had gotten two holes in it, each at different times. The first one was when Dora was at school. The sweater had caught on the corner of her desk. The other time was when she was  playing on the playground at the park. She had caught the sweater on a pole. Her mom had to sew the holes up the best that she could.

The sweater had also gotten lost once. Dora had been at her friend Marsha's house overnight. When she

 had packed up to go home the next day, she had not packed her sweater. She forgot about it until a few days later. It was very cold outside and she wanted to wear it. She looked all over the house, but couldn't find it anywhere.

After she thought about it, she remembered wearing it to Marsha's house. She called Marsha on the phone and, sure enough, it was there.

Dora loved the red sweater for many years, even when it no longer fit her. She kept it in a box with the rest of her special things. She planned to give it to her own little girl some day.

1. How did the sweater get the two holes in it?
2. How did the sweater get lost?
3. What did Dora do with the sweater when it no longer fit?

Paul Mows the Lawn

Paul's job was to mow the lawn. He had to do it once a week. It wasn't so bad, except when it was August. Then it was so hot that Paul didn't want to do it.

One hot day in August, Paul's dad said, "Paul, you know what today is."

"I know, Dad," said Paul. "It's the day that I have to mow the lawn."

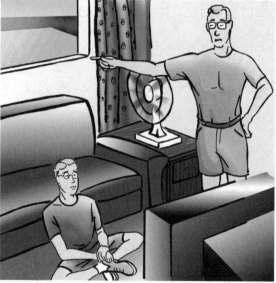

"The grass grows even in August," said Paul's dad.

"Yes, Dad," Paul said.

Paul went outside to get the mower out of the shed in the backyard. He thought that he would start with the back this time. It was bigger than the front, but then he would get the big part over with first. He started the mower and began mowing. After he finished mowing, he hauled the bags of grass to the front for trash pick-up day. Then, he took the mower to the front. The front yard was small, so it didn't take him

long. He hauled off the bags of grass and set them next to the others. At last, he was done.

When he got inside, Dad had a cold glass of lemonade waiting for him.

"Thanks, Dad," said Paul.

"You did a good job, Paul. Doesn't it feel great to be done?" asked Dad.

"Yes, at least for a week!" Paul said.

1. Why did Paul not like to mow in August?
2. What did Paul do with the bags of grass?
3. What did Dad have waiting for Paul when he was done?

The Neighbor In Number Eight

Jewel lived in an apartment with her mother, father, sister Leigh, and brother Andrew. They lived in apartment number seven. They had only lived there for a month.

Jewel and her brother and sister walked to school every day. They always passed by apartment number eight just before they went around the corner. They did not know the person who lived there. They had never seen whoever lived there. They knew that someone did live there because the mail was always taken in.

One day, on the way home from school, Andrew said, "I wonder who lives in number eight. I have never seen the person."

"I haven't either," said Leigh.

"Maybe we should knock on the door and see what happens," said Jewel.

They went up to the door of number eight and knocked. No one answered. They knocked again. Still no one answered. Then, they saw a lady peek out of the window in the door. She was gone as quickly as she had come.

"That must have been the lady who lives here," said Jewel.

"I wonder why she doesn't answer the door," said Andrew.

They knocked again.
This time, the lady opened
the door just a little bit.

"Hello," said Jewel.
"My name is Jewel and this
is my brother, Andrew, and
my sister, Leigh. We live next door to you."

"Yes, I know. I see you going to and from school every
day. My name is Mrs. Brewer."

She came out to talk to them. They found out that
Mrs. Brewer lived alone. She said that she didn't get
out much, except to go to the store. Jewel, Andrew,
and Leigh knew she needed some company.

After they left, they told their parents about Mrs.
Brewer.

"We will go over and meet her too. I'll bet that she would like some company," said Mom. "Why don't you kids visit her tomorrow after school? We can bake some cookies to take to her."

"She'd like that," said Leigh. "We'll go to see her tomorrow."

"Great," said Mom. "Now, let's get started on those cookies."

1. Where did Jewel and her family live?
2. Who did Jewel and her brother and sister see in number eight?
3. What were Jewel, Andrew, and Leigh going to do the next day?

The Brown House

Dow lives in a brown house. It's a small house with three bedrooms, a living room, kitchen, bathroom, and a basement. Dow likes his house very much. He likes the color brown.

Dow has a friend who lives down the street from him. His name is Chris. Chris likes to come to Dow's house and play. They play down in Dow's room in the basement. They like Dow's toy farm. The farm has

four brown cows that they like to play with.

They also like to play in the snow. They play outside, even when the wind blows and it is very cold. They like

to make a snowman. They always put Dow's brown hat on the snowman's head. If it is a girl snowman, they put a red bow around her neck.

There is an owl that lives in a tree in Dow's yard. Dow can hear the owl at night. He likes the sound that the owl makes.

Dow is happy in his brown house. He hopes that his family lives there for a long time.

1. What do Dow and Chris like to play with?
2. What do they like to make outside when it is snowy?
3. Why does Dow like his house?

The Snow Fort

Gil and his brother, John, liked the snow. They liked winter the best. They would always play outside after it had snowed. They made snowmen and threw snowballs at each other.

The best time that Gil and John had was when they made a snow fort. They made the walls of snow. They made windows in the snow walls.

Gil said, "John, I can see that you're having fun in our fort. Isn't it great?"

John said, "Yes. We're going to have fun in it as long as it is cold outside."

"Let's ask Mike and Ron if they want to have a snowball

fight. They're good at that.
We can be in our fort,"
said John.

Mike and Ron came over and
the boys had a snowball fight.
They had a lot of fun. Gil and John hid in their snow
fort. Mike and Ron hid behind the house.

Mike said, "Gil and John, you're good at this. That is a
neat fort. Ron and I are going to make one in our yard."

Mike and Ron went home to make their fort. Later,
they had Gil and John come over. They all played in
the fort. It was a fun day in the snow.

1. What season did Gil and John like best?
2. What did Gil and John make out of snow?
3. What did Gil and John do with Mike and Ron?

The Coin Collection

Boyd has a coin collection. He has been collecting coins for two years. He already has a lot of coins. He got some of them as gifts and he bought some of them at coin shops.

Boyd's grandpa was also a coin collector. He gave many of his coins to Boyd. There are coins from many different countries. Some of them are very old. Boyd likes to sit and look at them. He likes the way that they look. They are all different.

Boyd trades some of his coins for other ones. He joined a coin club. He trades coins with the other people in the club. One of his favorite coins is the one from Canada. It would be worth about ten cents in the USA. He got it from a boy in the coin club.

Boyd's coin collection gets bigger all of the time. He plans to keep collecting coins all of his life. Then he can pass it on to his children, just like Grandpa did for him.

1. How did Boyd get most of his coins?
2. Where did one of his favorite coins come from?
3. What does Boyd plan to do with his coin collection?

The Mouse in the House

One day, Jan thought she heard some scratching sounds in the house. She thought that she heard it coming from the wall in the kitchen. She went up close to the wall but didn't hear anything more.

The next day, she heard the sound again. This time, it was coming from the bathroom. She went in there and listened. She heard it again. She went and got Mom.

"Mom, listen. What do you hear?" asked Jan.

"I hear scratching," said Mom.

"What do you think it is?" asked Jan.

"I'll bet that it is a mouse," said Mom.

"You mean that we have a mouse in the house?" asked Jan.

"Yes. We'll have to find out where it is getting in," said Mom.

Jan and her mom checked all around the house. They found a small hole outside, over by the garage. Sure enough, a mouse had gotten in the house.

"I'll have to call the bug company," said Mom. "They will send someone out to get rid of the mouse," said Mom.

The next day, a man came to the house. He found the hole and got rid of the mouse. Mom was happy.

Mom said, "Dad will fix the hole. We hope that there will not be another mouse in our house."

1. What sound did the mouse make?
2. How did the mouse get in the house?
3. Who came out to get rid of the mouse?

Seeds in the Soil

Joy planted a flower garden. She planted pink, yellow, purple, and red flowers.

Joy started her garden by planting seeds in the soil. She planted the seeds in the spring, when it was starting to get warm. She didn't want to plant in cold soil. The flowers would start to come up in two weeks.

After the flowers started coming up, Joy wanted to plant something else. She asked her mom and dad if she could, and they said that it was all right. She wanted to plant something that she could eat, so she got some vegetable seeds. She carefully planted the vegetable seeds in the soil of her garden. She dug little holes in the soil and put the seeds in the holes. Then she covered the seeds up with soil and watered them.

In about three weeks, little vegetable plants started to come up out of the soil. There were carrots, peas, beans, and lettuce. Joy was excited about her vegetables. She couldn't wait until they grew big enough to pick and eat.

When the vegetables were big enough to eat, Joy and her mom picked the plants that were ready. They carefully pulled the plants out of the soil. They took

the plants into the house and washed them at the sink. Then they cut off the roots and any bad parts. Mom packed the vegetables in bags and put them in the refrigerator. Mom, dad, and Joy were happy to have fresh vegetables to eat.

Dad said, "You should plant a garden every spring, Joy. We like these vegetables."

Joy said, "I will, Dad. It was fun to plant the seeds in the soil and watch them grow."

1. What did Joy plant first?
2. How did Joy plant the vegetable seeds?
3. What did Mom and Joy do with the vegetables that were ready to pick?

Drew's Jewelry

Drew loved jewelry. She had necklaces, earrings, rings, bracelets, and pins. She kept them all in a pretty pink jewelry box on her dresser.

Drew had gotten most of her jewelry as gifts for her birthday and Christmas. Everyone knew that Drew loved jewelry, so that is what most people got for her.

Drew liked to play dress-up with her jewelry. She pretended that she was a queen or a princess. She would wear her crown with the red and green stones. Other times, she would pretend that she was a rich lady in a  big house. She would wear her necklace that looked like it was made of diamonds.

Drew's birthday was coming. She wanted a new pink

ring, one that was gold with a pink jewel. She had seen one in her favorite jewelry store at the mall. She showed her mom the ring when they were there.

Sure enough, Drew got the new pink ring for her birthday. She was very happy. She thought that it was the best present ever. She put the ring on her finger. It looked so pretty. She showed everyone the ring. She loved it.

Drew said, "Thanks, Mom. I love my new ring."

Mom said, "I knew that you would."

1. What kind of jewelry did Drew have?
2. Where did Drew keep her jewelry?
3. What did she get for her birthday?

Brown Stew

Cam's mom was making stew for supper. Cam wanted to help. She went into the kitchen and watched her mom cutting up the vegetables for the stew.

"Can I help?" Cam asked.

"Yes, you can," said Mom. "You can put these carrots and onions into the pot on the stove."

Cam put the cut-up carrots and onions into the big pot on the stove. Mom had not yet turned the heat on, so it was safe. Cam watched Mom cut some more vegetables. She still wanted to help.

"What else can I do?" Cam asked.

"Put the rest of the vegetables into the pot," Mom said.

Cam put the vegetables into the big pot. Mom started browning the stew meat in a pan on the stove.
The meat made a lot of noise while it was cooking.
Cam knew that her mom would not let her help with that, because the stove was hot.

After the meat was browned Mom put the meat into the big pot. She poured some brown gravy into the pot. She stirred it and put on the lid.

Cam asked, "When will the stew be done?"

"Not for two hours," Mom said.

"That is a long time," said Cam.

"Stew takes a long time to cook," said Mom.

When the stew was done, it was time to eat supper. Mom called Cam and Dad in to eat. The stew was so good!

Cam asked, "May we have this for supper tomorrow?"

"Yes," said Mom. "Then it will be called leftovers!"

1. How did Cam help to make the stew?
2. How long did the stew take to cook?
3. How were Cam and her mom cooking safely when they were making the stew?